AUSTRALIAN VERSE FOR THE YOUNG

By Bindi-Bindi
Illustrated by Lynne Wilson

Published by
BINDI-BINDI PUBLISHING
63 HAMLYN ROAD
OAKEY, QLD. 4401
(07) 4691 2317

First Printing 2000

Printed in Australia by

Blueprint Australia Pty Ltd
Phone: (02) 9844 5407

Reprint Number 9

Author's Note

We are living in a world spinning out of control, with many of the old-fashioned values fast disappearing. The very fabric of human society seems to be coming apart. Today's world demands much of the young, rushing them through childhood with little time to establish real values.

In this, our second volume, we have endeavoured to present some primary lessons in a fun way, and give children a glimpse of yesteryear Australia. We have again used our unique fauna as the principal characters; and have included a helpful Glossary.

It is our sincere wish that *Australian Verse for the Young* will bring some knowledge and some pleasure to our young readers.

BINDI-BINDI PUBLISHING

About the Artist

Lynne Wilson lives with her family in Gympie, Queensland and has had considerable success as an artist. Lynne especially enjoys the challenge that Commissions present. She can then apply her talents in harmonizing a variety of concepts to produce a complete work.

We at Bindi-Bindi have greatly valued Lynne's enthusiasm and considerable input which have contributed so much to the making of . . .

Australian Verse for the Young.

Contents

A Message to Each Child

We hope you'll enjoy this book of verse,
Some poems are wordy, others quite terse,
But our fauna is there for you to enjoy,
So come and meet them – don't be coy.

And whenever you open this picture book,
And at each of these creatures, you take a look,
Make them your friends, and you will find,
That animals, like people, will respond if you're kind.

This book belongs to:

_____

_____

_____

At the Beach

A big Brown Snake, and a Crocodile
went to the beach, to play a while.
And in their swimsuits, they looked so slim,
as down to the water, they went for a swim.

But as they went in, the people leapt out,
with squeals and shrieks, and many a shout.
They rushed up the beach, leaving brolly and towel,
dragging children behind, who started to howl.

So the Snake and the Croc, up the beach they rushed too,
trying to fathom, this great hullabaloo.

For whatever was causing these people such shock,
was not going to get this Snake or this Croc.

The Bush Gymnasium

Some fauna from the Australian Bush,
for a healthy body decided to push.
"Exercise is the thing we need,
just follow me, I'll take the lead,
push-ups, skipping and aerobics too,
and plenty of jumping," said Kangaroo.

Snake said, "Wriggling keeps one slim."
But Echidna thought it just a whim.
Emu said, "Bending close to the ground
is the best way to trim, that I've ever found."
"Standing on one foot is the best," said Crane,
"If you follow my system, no weight will you gain."

"Oh, swimming is the best way," said Slippery Eel,
"Go swimming each day and those pounds
you will peel."
"I think flying's the answer," said Mrs Black Crow,
"With flying each day, your waist will not grow."

Then from somewhere nearby came an
audible moan,
a very deep sigh that stopped them
like stone.
"If it takes all that effort,
to stop getting fat,
let's stay as we are," said
sleepy Wombat.

So one from another, each took his farewell,
    it was plain to see, what their faces did tell.
    They wandered off slowly, each looking so glum,
for that was the end of their gymnasium.

The Tennis Match at Snake Gully

A Wallaby and a Kangaroo, decided to play a set or two.
So out they went onto the court,
  with racquets and balls and a single thought:
to win the game, no matter the cost,
  for there'd be no glory, for the one who lost.

A Magpie sat at each end
of the net,
to call to the Umpire, in case
of a let.

For linesmen, the Emus and
Brolgas stood tall,
watching to see where each ball
would fall.
Or in case of a footfault, or other mistake,
that Kanga or Walla, were likely to make.

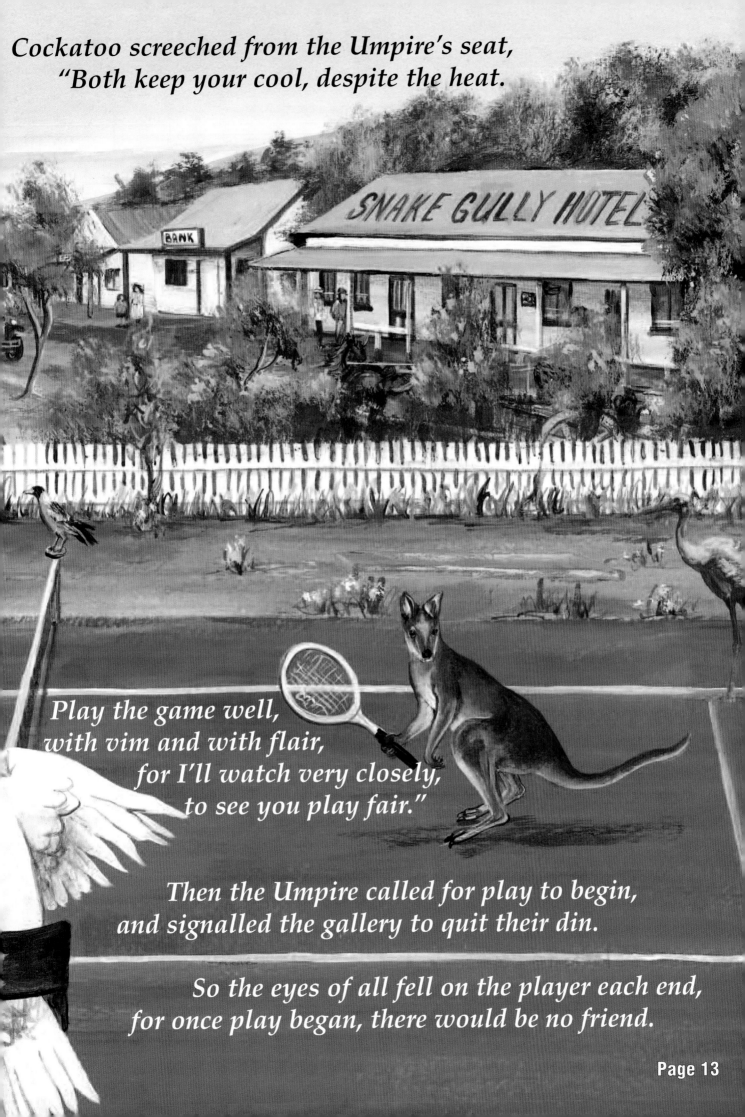

Cockatoo screeched from the Umpire's seat,
"Both keep your cool, despite the heat.

Play the game well,
with vim and with flair,
    for I'll watch very closely,
        to see you play fair."

Then the Umpire called for play to begin,
and signalled the gallery to quit their din.

So the eyes of all fell on the player each end,
for once play began, there would be no friend.

Kanga's first serve,
    was a withering ace,
    and for the first few games,
    set a blistering pace.
It did not look good for the Wallaby small,
for Kanga was fast, and he stood
    very tall.

But Walla, though small,
had a very big heart,
and he played with real
courage, right from the start.
Spectators cheered loudly, from up
in the stand,
and Walla responded with his
lightning backhand.
With volleys and forehands, and
occasional lob,
he showed all the fans, he was
no tennis slob.

But as the day wore on, the sun got hot,
both players were tired, but the crowd was not.
It was two sets each, and five games all,
tension was mounting, with all eyes on the ball.
Several moved forward, to the spectators rail,
for at any moment, one player must fail.

But big clouds had gathered, it became quite dark,
and the dogs in the grandstand began to bark.

Then down poured the rain, it came
helter and skelter,
so all on the court had to rush
for the shelter.

It poured and it poured, and it poured some more,
and the water rose to the grandstand floor.
And while all agreed it was the end of the game,
to go home now, would be such a shame.

So the ducks set out to enjoy the new lake,
not to mention the geese, and a big water snake.
The pigs sloshed about, with other
animals too,
and in no time at all, it looked like a stew.

So Kanga and Walla, they too joined the fun,
it mattered no more, which of them had won.
They splashed and they hollered,
and they rushed all about,
throwing mud at each other, with many a shout.

And when the moon came out
on that muddy scene,
all present agreed, a great day it had been.
So when players discuss their games
with great zest,
that game at Snake Gully, is voted the best.

Little Bilby

To Wally Wallaby, said our little Bilby,
"As tall as you are, is as tall as I will be."
But said Wally Wallaby to our little Bilby,
"As tall as you're now,
is as tall as you'll still be."

So if you're not tall,
or you may be quite small,
there are important lessons to be learnt by us all.
So take comfort in knowing, and try to recall,
that if you fall over,
it's not far to fall.

For as you travel the highway of life,
you'll have some gladness,
you'll learn about strife.
But as you walk on,
what will set you apart,
is not how TALL,
but how BIG is your HEART.

Sylvester Seagull

Sylvester Seagull is a very fine bird,
about this fellow, I'm sure that you've heard?
He's quite at home on the wide sandy beach,
and as each wave approaches, he jumps out of reach.

Moving quickly along as the waves are receding,
he's never so busy as when he is feeding.
He picks up here, he darts in there,
for Sylvester Seagull,
there's plenty of fare.

In his fresh white shirt, and his smart grey coat,
just like the pelicans he loves to float.
And when boats come in on the morning tide,
there'll be some pickings come over the side.

Then all the gulls will come wheeling and diving;
yes, down by the ocean these seagulls are thriving.
With their bright red legs and bright red feet,
if you go to the seaside, you'll be bound to meet.

The Aussie Barbecue

A Lyrebird and a Cockatoo decided to have a barbecue.

But they had no meat, and they had no fish;

all they had was an empty dish.

So they made a list of the things they'd need,
and the friends they'd invite, to have a good feed.
They'd buy some meat,
        and they'd catch some fish,
get bread and buns to
        fill their dish.

"We'll need some plates,
        and some pannikins too,
and we'll need some tea to make a brew.
        We'll get some biscuits and
                crackers and drinks,
                        and have it all here before
                                the sun sinks."

So they got it all ready, the time was now here,
for guests were arriving,
to spread some good cheer.
"We had better hurry, the fire to light."
But the wood was quite wet,
no kindling in sight.

So the Lyrebird puffed,
and the Pheasant
        he blew,

    but the leaves only smouldered,
no flame would come through.
    So they began to
        fan with the Pheasant's tail,
    until their strength began to fail.

    Then through the smoke,
            and his watering eyes,
        A bright red tin, the Cockatoo spies.
            "A'ha" he said, "this is what we need;
    in no time at all, we'll have our feed."

So he took off the lid
and began to pour,
and in no time at all, how that fire did roar.
The flames leapt up and burnt the meat black,
while guests in their panic,
began to push back.

Poor Potaroo was petrified,
and Goanna acted crazed.

The Pheasant said,
"Not pleasant."

as he watched that fire blaze.

The Pigmy Possum postured,
the Frilly Lizard froze,
The Tassie Devil, terrified,
rushed off to get a hose.

Lizard started laughing,
    it seemed like quite a joke,
        to see Koala coughing;
            his lungs half full of smoke.
When Pheasant's tail caught fire; it gave him such a fright,

while the blackened
face of Cockatoo,

was such a
sorry
sight.

So if you plan a barbecue,
    and invite your dearest friends,
make sure the wood is nice and dry,
        have kindling
            without end.

Or even if you have to
    get a barbecue on hire,
        do not allow a single guest,
            to put petrol on the fire.

The Apostle Birds

The Apostle birds, often twelve in their number,
seem to chatter all day,   and seldom to slumber.
Their dress is quite drab,
but they keep on the run,

always so
happy, and
ready for fun.

COOLA

So what can we learn, from these happy birds?
Is there some wisdom, we can put into words?
Are you quite poor, with little to wear?
Is no one listening to your silent prayer?

It's best to remember, we don't all stand out.
For most, there's no cheering, not even a shout.
While it takes many small grains,
to make one lovely beach,
With the one lonely starfish, just out of reach.

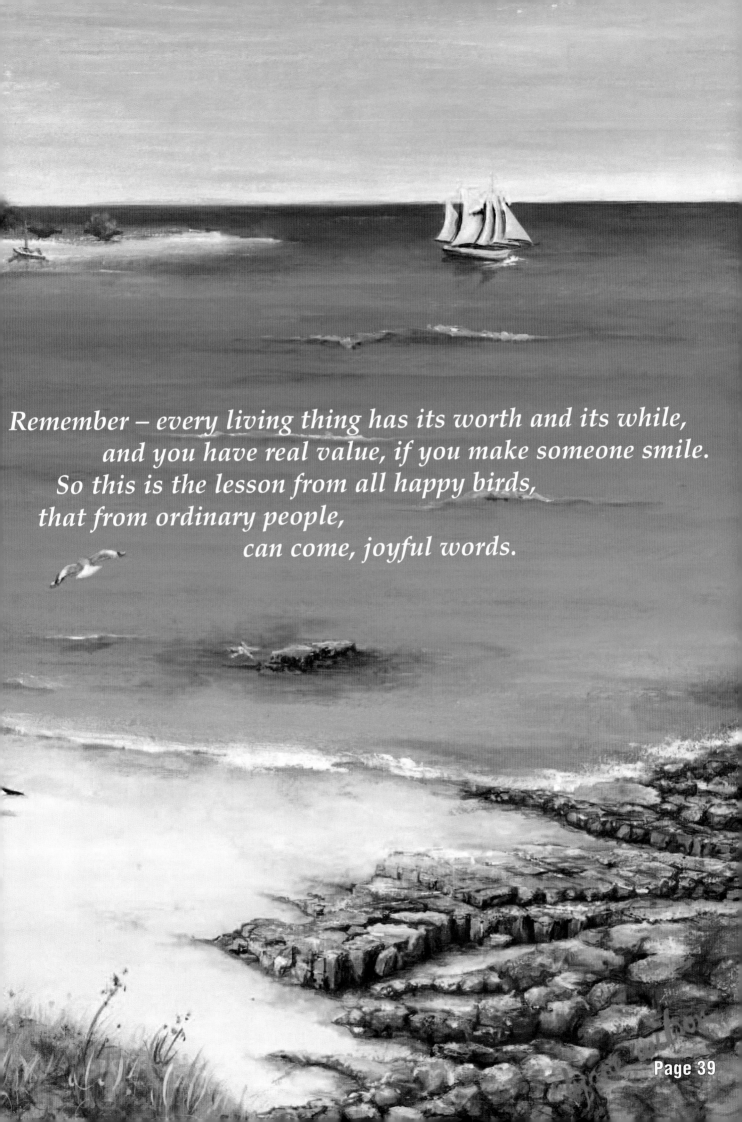

Remember – every living thing has its worth and its while,
and you have real value, if you make someone smile.
So this is the lesson from all happy birds,
that from ordinary people,
can come, joyful words.

The Kakadu Bush Band

If Bandicoot can
play the flute,
I think O'Possum
can play the lute.

I know Echidna can bang a drum,
and Kanga has a guitar to strum.

With Wallaby on the violin,
  the Jabirus can make a din.
Let Emu blow on the didgeridoo,
  while Mrs Crane taps with her shoe.

The Frogs can give us some throaty croaks,
while the Brolgas dance in their feathered cloaks.

The Lyrebirds
can sway
and sing,
to the haunting
sounds of the
Bell Birds ring.

Big crocodile can thump the floor,
while Cockatoo conducts the score.

The Pelicans can stamp their feet,
so lets all hurry to get a seat.
For the players are ready to do their part,
the Kakadu Bush Band is about to start.

Donny Dolphin

Donny Dolphin swims so fast,
a sailing boat he can easily pass.
He leaps and dives, and goes like a Packet,
he's really quite dry, in his waterproof jacket.

He's smooth and sleek, his skin in so shiny,
he's happy as Larry, out there in the briny.
He'll chatter and squeak, has a cute little beak,
but if you get too close, he's off like a streak.

At the Porpoise Pool, they go to school,
tricks they learn, they are so cool.
You can touch their face, a ball they will chase,
then leap in the air,
with considerable grace.

Then swim back with a grin,
"Why don't you come in?"
They seem to say, as you tickle their chin.
"Just hop on my back,
and we'll go for a spin,
you'll enjoy the ride."
says Donny Dolphin.

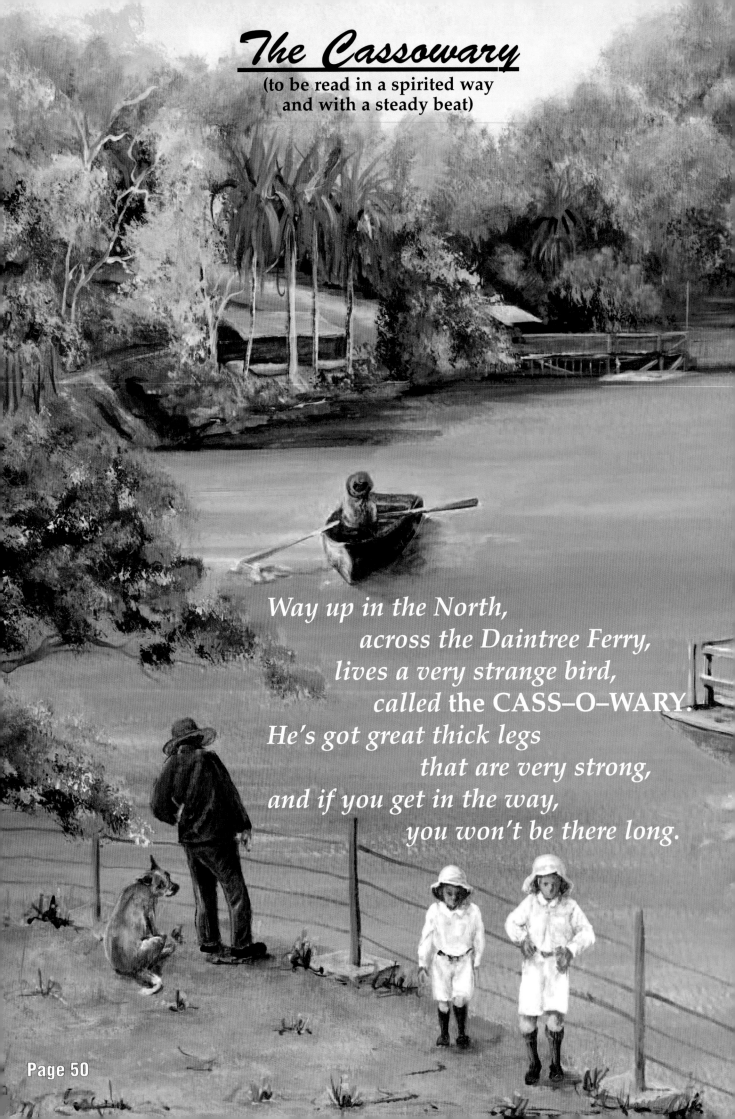

The Cassowary

**(to be read in a spirited way
and with a steady beat)**

Way up in the North,
  across the Daintree Ferry,
 lives a very strange bird,
   called the CASS–O–WARY.
He's got great thick legs
   that are very strong,
and if you get in the way,
   you won't be there long.

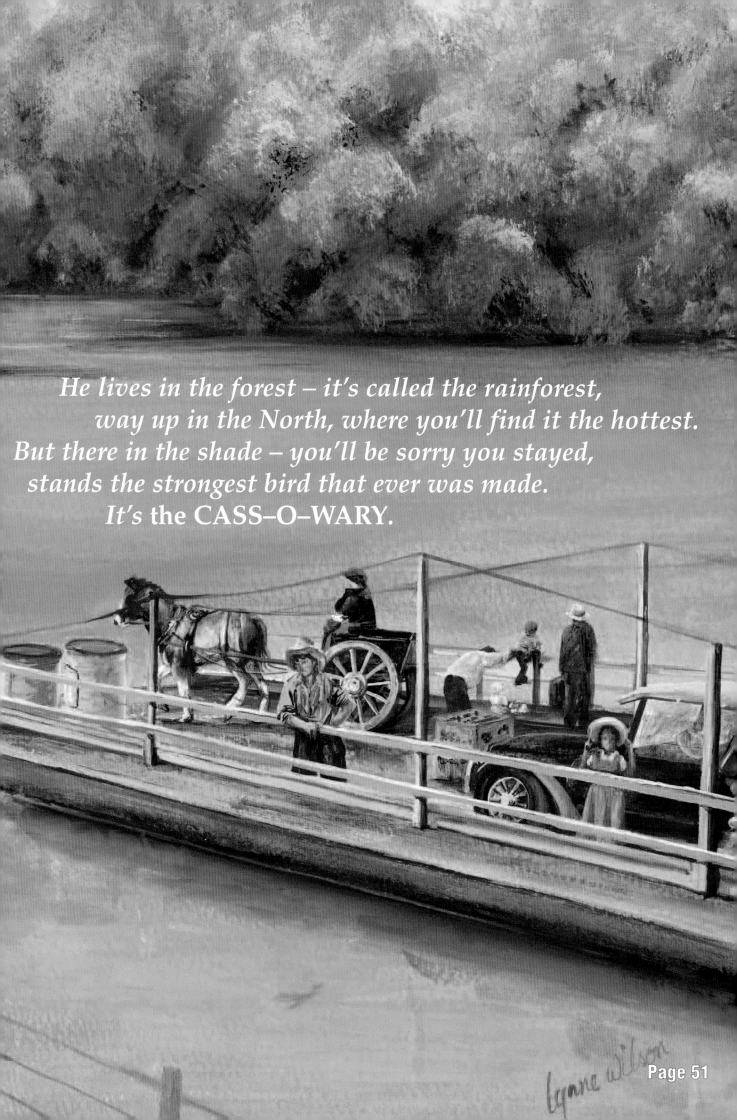

He lives in the forest – it's called the rainforest,
way up in the North, where you'll find it the hottest.
But there in the shade – you'll be sorry you stayed,
stands the strongest bird that ever was made.
It's the CASS–O–WARY.

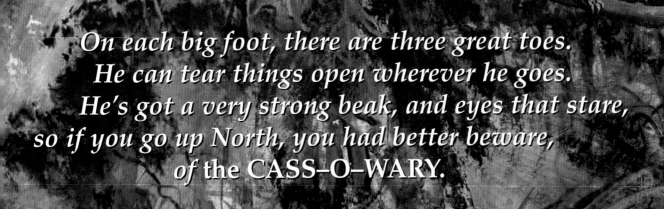

On each big foot, there are three great toes.
He can tear things open wherever he goes.
He's got a very strong beak, and eyes that stare,
so if you go up North, you had better beware,
of the CASS–O–WARY.

It stands about four feet tall, being muscle and all,
if you try to outrun it, you'll be bound to fall.
He may not fly, but he can run like Harry,
so don't you go near, that there,
CASS–O–WARY.

On top of it's head there's a helmet sat,
if you come face to face, you'll know where you're at.
So take my advice and never do tarry,
where that strange bird lives;

It's called
the CASS–O–WARY!

Page 4   **WINDMILL** This trusted wind-driven water pump is as synonymous with Australia as are the other famous Windmills with the Netherlands. More common in Outback Australia, but also found on the Coast where underground water is available. The Great Artesian basin and other aquafers are vitally important to Australia, which is considered the driest continent on Earth.

Page 5-7   **BROWN SNAKE** One of Australia's most venomous snakes (the Taipan is the deadliest snake in Australia). The Brown can grow to 2.1 metres and range in colour from light brown to almost black, and has a cream underbelly. As many Australian snakes are poisonous, it is better to avoid all of them. Remember, most snakes will try to escape unless they are cornered, so slowly back away to safety.

   CROCODILE There are two principal species in Australia. The small Freshwater or Johnston River Crocodile, easily recognised by its narrow snout is relatively harmless, while the Salt Water Crocodile which can grow to 6.0 metres is literally a man-eater. Both species flourish in the rivers of Northern Australia. The largest Salt Water crocodile on record (8.5 metres) was shot by a woman in the Norman River, near Normanton, in North West Queensland.

Page 8   **EMU** This largest of Australian birds, resembling the African Ostrich, is usually found in the Australian Outback, where it grazes over large areas. After the female lays the eggs, the male does the brooding which is usually eight weeks. When travelling through the Outback, it is not unusual to see an adult pair with several chicks at heel.

Page 8,9   **KANGAROO** Probably the animal most associated with Australia. It is the largest of this family of grazing animals, ranging down to Wallabies, Quokkas, Bettongs, Pademelons and smaller. Some main groups are Eastern Grey, Western Grey and Red. Males can grow to 2.4 metres and weigh 70kg. The female has a distinctive front pouch, concealing four teats, where it suckles a single Joey for about six months. The Kangaroo's powerful back legs enable it to cover considerable distances quickly in great bounds, using its heavy tail for balance. The Kangaroo is featured with the Emu on the Australian Coat of Arms.

   ECHIDNA (E–KID–NA) Also called SPINY ANTEATER. This cat-sized animal is not to be confused with the larger European Porcupine. The back of the Echidna is covered with fur and many vertical spines. It licks up termites with its fast-moving tongue. As with the Platypus, the Echidna also lays an egg, which is then kept in its brood pouch. When hatched, the baby can suck up milk exuded from glands within the pouch.

   BROLGA (AUSTRALIAN CRANE) The name comes from the Aboriginal Dreamtime character Bralgah (the girl who always danced). This tall and elegant bird is famous for its graceful courtship dancing, often in "Corroboree". It is a powerful flier, but must run to gain speed for take-off. It frequents grasslands and swampy places, feeding on frogs, small reptiles and herbage. Average height is 1.0 metre with a wingspan of 1.8 metres.

   EEL This smooth skinned snake-like fish is found in fresh and salt water. While its appearance is not very inviting it is good eating, and some species reach a length of 1.8 metres.

   CROW This shiny black bird of the Raven family grows to 45cm. Its call is a loud cawing cry, at times ending in a drawn out gargle. This scavenger is found Australia wide, at times by the roadside where dead Fauna can provide a ready meal.

Page 10,11   **WOMBAT** A large burrowing Marsupial, weighing up to 40kg. It is shy by nature, and is seldom seen in the wild. It is a nocturnal feeder on grasses and roots. The female has a rear-opening pouch which conceals two teats, where it suckles its young for about six months.

Page 12,13   **WALLABY** A smaller version of the Kangaroo but with their own characteristics. There are several species including Rock, Parma, Nailtail, Brush, Agile and Pretty Face.

   MAGPIE This common Australian bird, a little smaller than the Crow, has a delightful carolling call. It is in variations of black and white, and can be easily tamed to take food from the hand, but at nesting time it can become quite aggressive to passers-by.

   COCKATOO This large white parrot with its sulphur yellow crest grows to about 50cm and is a popular pet. It can be trained to imitate human speech, but its raucous screeching does not please the neighbours. In the wild, it flocks in large numbers and can do considerable damage to crops.

Page 20,21   **BILBY** This is a member of the Bandicoot family, but has silky hair and long ears. Found in arid areas of Australia, it must get moisture from its food. It is a strong burrower, making deep tunnels where it remains during the day, venturing out after dark to feed. The female has a rear opening pouch to suckle its young.

     THORNY DEVIL This rather bizarre specimen is not as dangerous as it looks. Apart from any defence advantage, some authorities suggest that the horns and spikes may help channel water to the creatures mouth, which would be useful in its arid habitat.

     DINGO A Primitive dog introduced into Australia prior to white settlement. It is an intelligent hunter about the size of a large dog. It can range in colour from creamy to almost black. The Dingo has at times reached plague proportions, moving the Australian Government to place a bounty on its head. In a further attempt to limit its spread and to protect the large sheep population, the Government erected the longest fence in the world, stretching some 5,500kms from Ceduna in South Australia to Dalby in Queensland.

Page 22-25   **SEAGULL (SILVER GULL)** This familiar seabird is common around the Australian coast and is synonymous with a day at the beach. While its natural diet is small fish, it has found ready pickings at rubbish tips, which is a sad situation for this pristine bird. They are often the uninvited guests at the beachside picnic or BBQ and will follow fishing boats, diving for tidbits coming over the side.

Page 24,25   **PELICAN** This very large seabird usually seen along the coast, can also be found on inland waterways where it goes to breed and raise its young. It uses its bag-like bill to scoop up fish, which it swallows whole. A favourite with visitors, it can grow to 1.2 metres, with a wing span of 1.5 metres. They often follow fishing boats in the hope of a free meal. The most delightful picture is to see them drifting along against a backdrop of colourful boats at anchor.

Page 26-35   **LYRE BIRD (SUPERB LYRE BIRD)** This ground dwelling bird is most often found in the Eucalypt forests of South Eastern Australia. About the size of the pheasant, the male uses its Lyre shaped tail as a canopy as it courts the female, singing an almost endless repertoire of songs. Its amazing ability to mimic other bird songs as well as sounds of human origin, has given rise to the false notion that it is the <u>LIAR</u> bird.

Page 27   **PANNIKIN** Metal drinking cup used in early Australian times.

Page 28-35   **POTOROO** These pint-sized members of the Kangaroo/Wallaby family come in several species. They are found in many coastal areas of Australia, including Tasmania. They are generally grey-brown in colouring and are nocturnal feeders on insects, berries and roots. The female carries her single young in a pouch which conceals four teats.

     GOANNA (AUSTRALIAN MONITOR) There are more than twenty species ranging in size from 15cm to more than 1.2 metres (including tail). They are not dangerous, and if approached, will dash off or scale the nearest tree. Some aquatic species have a strong tail which is used laterally as an aid to swimming.

     PHEASANT This common bird belongs to the world-wide family of Partridges, Peafowl and Quolls, so is not native to Australia, but is now found in great numbers in forest areas, grassy plains and swamplands. The Ring-necked is probably the most common.

     PIGMY POSSOM These tiny members of the Possum family can roll themselves into a fluffy ball to fit into the hand. Nocturnal feeders on insects, fruit, berries and nectar, they use their tail to great advantage as they move from branch to branch. Females have a nursing pouch and can produce two or more litters per year.

     FRILLED LIZARD Best known for its bright orange/red frill or collar, which, when extended, can give this small lizard a quite threatening appearance. Like many lizards, it spends most of its life in trees searching for insects. If you surprise one on the ground, it will run off, upright on its back legs to climb the nearest tree. It is the Reptile Emblem of Australia.

     TASSIE DEVIL The name makes them sound worse than they are. However, they have never been sought after as family pets. These rather fierce-looking residents of the Island State of Tasmania, display a rather frightening array of teeth in their oversize jaws. Their diet includes almost anything into which they can sink those teeth, from grass to dead animal carcasses. They are usually black with a white splash on the chest and lower back. The female will carry three or four young on her back. At feeding times, there is usually a lot of snapping and snarling, but any wounds inflicted on fellow guests are not usually serious.

     KOALA This furry favourite hardly needs any introduction, as it is now found in Animal Parks around the World. It is always presented as a cuddly "bear", but is correctly a Marsupial. It has a pouch for nursing its young, even though the female is often seen with a baby clinging to her back. It has long sharp claws for climbing, but there have been cases where people have been severely injured trying to capture Koalas in the wild. Koalas sleep quite comfortably high in their favourite Eucalypt trees.

Page 36,37   **APOSTLE BIRDS** (Also called HAPPY FAMILY BIRDS) These ground feeders are found mainly in Eastern Australia's inland areas. The family size of twelve has been observed so often so as to give them their Biblical name. Despite their rather drab appearance, they seem always to be happy and busy, chattering away as they share in family duties of nest building and raising their young.

Page 38,39   **TURTLES** (not to be confused with the ponderous land Tortoise) They come in a wide range of species and sizes, from the tiny freshwater turtle found in coastal streams, to the great ocean-going Loggerheads and Green Turtles. Some Australian beaches have become famous for turtle hatchings, none more so than Mon-Repos near Bundaberg, Queensland. The freshwater species grow to about 30cm, while their sea-going cousins reach a length of 1.5 metres.

Page 40,41   **BANDICOOT** There are several species ranging in colour from brown to greyish-black. It has coarse hair and a short tail and is about the size of a domestic cat, but with a long pointed nose. It is a night feeder on insects, worms and herbage. The female nurses its young in a rear-opening pouch.

                    POSSUM This furry Australian comes in several species and sizes, the largest being the Ring-tail and the Brush-tail. The latter is fairly easy to tame if offered pieces of fruit and other tasty morsels, although they can become a nuisance if allowed indoors.

Page 42   **BELL BIRD** These small birds, so hard to detect in their forest surrounds, give out the most delightful and haunting bell-like call. One of four species of Miner Bird, it has yellowish-green feathers, khaki green wings, and yellow beak and legs.

Page 42-47   **JABIRU** This is the only Australian Stork and is found mainly across Northern Australia. This beautiful bird with its 1.8 metre wingspan, has become the symbol of the Northern Territory and its famous Kakadu Wetlands. Its call resembles a low gutteral boom.

Page 46   **PACKET** A fast mail boat of yesteryear.

Page 46,47   **DIDGERIDOO** This now famous Aboriginal musical instrument, is simply a length of small hollow tree about 1.2 metres long. It takes skill and patience to master this primitive instrument. The sound produced is like no other, and it has become a popular souvenir of Australia, especially if hand-painted in the traditional Aboriginal style.

Page 46-49   **DOLPHIN** In 66AD Greek writer Plutarch stated that the Dolphin had a gift for unselfish friendship. Down through the succeeding centuries this observation has been verified again and again. In modern times these delightful sea-mammals have enthralled people at Aquatic Parks around the world. But what gives people special happiness is to be able to associate with Dolphins in their wild environment. Three locations in Australia where this is happening are: Monkey Mia in Western Australia; Tangalooma Wild Dolphin Resort on Moreton Island, Queensland; and Tin Can Bay near Gympie in Queensland. Sadly, this beautiful creature is becoming an endangered species, as the use of drift nets and other human activities reduce their numbers by an estimated 500,000 annually, a tragedy of mammoth proportions that <u>must be stopped</u>. Can you help?

Page 50-52   **CASSOWARY** This seldom seen bird is found in the Rain Forests of North Queensland and New Guinea. While usually shy, it becomes a fearless aggressor if cornered or threatened. It is a very strong bird, equipped with blade-like inner toes. Like the Emu it is flightless, but with its unique helmet, it is able to bash its way through the undergrowth at speed. The female is larger and more brightly plumed than the male, reaching a height of 1.5 metres. When one hears its low gutteral call, its time to leave.

CONCLUSION

DO YOU NOT AGREE THAT THE COUNTLESS MARVELS IN THE NATURAL WORLD AROUND US, GIVE OVERWHELMING EVIDENCE OF BRILLIANT DESIGN BY A LOVING AND INTELLIGENT CREATOR?